This bo

D0419019

HAPPILY NEVER
AFTER...

Modern Cautionary Verse

MITCHELL SYMONS

DOUBLEDAY

HAPPILY NEVER AFTER
A DOUBLEDAY BOOK 978 0 857 53270 1

Published in Great Britain by Doubleday,
an imprint of Random House Children's Publishers UK
A Random House Group Company

This edition published 2013

1 3 5 7 9 10 8 6 4 2

The Random House Group Limited supports the Forest Stewardship Council® (FSC®),
the leading international forest-certification organisation. Our books carrying the FSC label
are printed on FSC®-certified paper. FSC is the only forest-certification scheme supported
by the leading environmental organisations, including Greenpeace. Our paper procurement
policy can be found at www.randomhouse.co.uk/environment

MIX
Paper from
responsible sources
FSC® C016897
FSC
www.fsc.org

Set in Century Schoolbook

RANDOM HOUSE CHILDREN'S PUBLISHERS UK
61–63 Uxbridge Road, London W5 5SA

www.randomhousechildrens.co.uk
www.randomhouse.co.uk

Addresses for companies within The Random House Group Limited can be found at: www.
randomhouse.co.uk/offices.htm

THE RANDOM HOUSE GROUP Limited Reg. No. 954009

A CIP catalogue record for this book is available from the British Library.

Printed and bound in the UK by Clays Ltd, St Ives plc

To you, dear reader.
Enjoy the poems but heed the lessons!

Introduction

When I was a boy – and I'll add the words 'many many years ago' before anyone else does – I was a huge fan of Hilaire Belloc's *Cautionary Verses*.

If you've never read them, then I hope that the very least this book achieves is to lead you to them. There you will find such gems as:

Jim: Who ran away from his Nurse, and was eaten by a Lion.

Henry King: Who chewed bits of String, and was early cut off in Dreadful Agonies.

Matilda: Who told Lies, and was Burned to Death.

Godolphin Horne: Who was cursed with the Sin of Pride, and Became a Boot-Black.

And my own favourite: *Rebecca: Who slammed Doors For Fun And Perished Miserably.*

A while ago, I was clearing out a box of treasured possessions from my childhood when I came across a well-thumbed copy of *Cautionary Verses* and mused to myself, *I bet some clever clogs has updated these poems and made themselves a fortune.*

So I put the words 'cautionary' and 'verses' into Google, and then, for good measure, into Amazon – and, incredibly, *nothing came up*!

I told my publishers, who raised the (not unreasonable) objections that a) they weren't my poems to update, and b) I was the man who delivered trivia – since when was I a poet?

In response (and thinking quickly on my feet), I did two things. I pointed out that I wasn't going to *update* the poems as such . . . Oh no, I was going to, er, write completely (gulp) *new* cautionary verses.

I then went away and wrote *Tiffany: Who couldn't put down her Mobile Telephone and died a Horrible Death.*

With all modesty, I thought I'd done a pretty good job, but I was unprepared for the reaction from my publishers and, more importantly, their sales team. They loved it. People – many of whom had nothing to do with commissioning the book – were passing it around the office. It even found its way onto Facebook.

Could I please write some more?

Emboldened, I found I could.

Look, don't get me wrong, I still don't think of myself as a poet, but I reckon I've managed to get some humour out of modern-day foibles while maintaining rhymes and (usually) scansion. At the very least, I think I managed to get the right number of syllables to each line. Count 'em if you like: God knows, I did!

You'll also notice that the poems are often more than a little brutal. Did children *really* deserve death merely for overusing their mobile phones or for employing the Australian inflection? Obviously not – though I still reserve judgement for people who say 'haitch' instead of 'aitch' for the eighth letter of the alphabet.

However, if I was going to be faithful to the thrust and tone of Belloc's original – and although he was writing for children, he wasn't pulling his punches (the clues being in such expressions as *eaten by a Lion, cut off in Dreadful Agonies, Burned to Death* and *Perished Miserably*) – then I was going to have silence my qualms and dish out wildly disproportionate punishments (though I believe that NO punishment would be too great for – to take just three of my 'victims' – Sebastian, Freddie and Callum).

Now for some people who deserve plaudits – not punishments.

They are: my wonderful editor, Lauren Buckland, my wife, Penny (who contributed a couple of fine lines to Chelsea), my lovely publisher, Annie Eaton, designer Dominica Clements and illustrator Steve Wells.

In addition, I'd also like to thank the following people for their help, contributions and/or support: Gilly Adams, Lauren Bennett, Jenny Garrison,

Bryn Musson, Charlie Symons, Jack Symons, Louise Symons, Harriet Venn and Rob Woolley.

If I've missed anyone out, then please know that it is, as I always say, entirely down to my own stupidity.

Mitchell Symons
www.mitchellsymons.com

Contents

Tiffany: Who couldn't put down her Mobile Telephone and died a Horrible Death

A sight that's known to generate moans
Is silly girls on mobile phones.
Ignoring people in the street,
They map their lives in every tweet.
They text each other the latest saga
Of love and shopping and Lady Gaga.
They use the latest apparatus
To update their Facebook status:
Just got out from taking a shower –
It only took me half an hour!

Tiffany Smith was one such girl.
She spent her life in a social whirl.
Wherever she went, she used her phone –
In school and out, you'd hear its tone.
Justin Bieber's latest hit
Would indicate the dial's lit.
Her BFF just calling to say:
'I'm going to phone you later today.'

Tiffany **had** to keep in touch:
Talking and texting meant so much –
For her the stakes were life and death.
To speak to Katie, Charlotte and Beth
Sixty, seventy times a day
Was not excessive – unless you pay.
And here, alas – the bitter pill:
It wasn't Tiff who paid the bill.
That task befell her struggling mother
Who also provided for Tiffy's brother

(Another child to nag and drain her:
For him it was always the latest trainer).

Her phone bill was a source of woe:
Not for her the Pay-and-Go,
Tiff had a tariff – it was second to none,
And yet she always came undone:
A thousand minutes wouldn't last a week.
If only Tiff didn't have to speak
To every friend throughout the day:
'Hi, it's Tiffy, just phoned to say "Hi" –
I'll text you later to tell you why.'
And that is what she would always do,
Signing off: *LUV* (space) *U*.
Tiff was an expert at textual speech –
No word or phrase was beyond her reach.
ROFL, LOL and OMG
Came to her so easily.

Until, one day, as we shall see,
It proved to be a calamity.
While she crossed a busy junction,
Her mind was on another function.
As she texted her bestie Kylie
And entered in a final smiley,
A Ford Ka knocked her off her feet.
It killed her. End of tweet.
When car hits girl, the former wins –
Tiff was knocked right off her pins.
Her head was smashed, her neck
    was broken,
Her final 'Heya' went unspoken.
Tiffany was DEFINITELY dead,
And all those words were left unsaid:
No TTYLs; no BRBs –
Well, not when your head's wrapped
round your knees.

The driver stopped, got out the car,
Dazed and shocked, the way you are.
You couldn't really blame the bloke –
He wasn't speeding, but how sick's
    this joke?
At point of impact, he was having
    a moan
While talking on a hands-free phone!

At her funeral, the priest intones,
'Please turn off your mobile phones.'
His words cause Tiffy's friends to leave –
They need their phones to help them grieve.
It seems they still don't get the truth
(It's always hard to teach the youth):
There's a time and place to use a phone,
Preferably when you're on your own,
Sitting down in reflective mode –
Not walking across a busy road.

For if Tiffany's life was not in vain,
Other girls must avoid her pain
And listen to parents and not get vexed
When told not to phone and not to text.

Freddie Lock: Whose Swearing so shocked his grandparents that it cost him a Fortune when they won the Lottery

A fault in boys that's hard to bear
Is when they never cease to swear.
A guilty child was Freddie Lock,
Who loved to swear and so to shock.

He used such words as **snick*** and **bork**,*
And **bankle**,* **trup*** and even **snork**.*
You could go east, west, north or south
And not meet such a potty mouth.

* Author's note: I am no fool. I have used made-up words
in place of Freddie's swear words. What you use is up to you,
but make sure you avoid Freddie's fate . . .

His parents, Catherine and Tom,
Did not know where he got it from.
OK, it's true they sometimes cursed:
'Damn' or 'Rats' at their very worst.

They thought his friends might be
          to blame,
But next to Freddie, they were tame.
Just ordinary boys of nine
Who say 'Bum' or words from books
          like mine.

Freddie's gran – now she was tough,
A woman made of sterner stuff.
She'd been a teacher in her youth
And wasn't scared to speak the truth.

'That boy is unbelievable!
You let him? Inconceivable!
Can't you see the slippery slope?
Let's clean his mouth – I'll get the soap!'

Freddie, hearing his granny cross,
Smiled and said, 'Who gives a toss?
What can that *pumpty** do to me?
She's just a numpty – can't you see?'

Freddie's grandpa entered the fray:
'I can't believe the things you say.
Lucky your dad was not like you –
I'd have beaten him black and blue.'

'Unlucky **wonkat**,'* Freddie said.
'We're living now – not then. You're dead!
Drak* off while I play with my toys –
Why do old **crots*** make so much noise?'

Their son Tom said, 'Don't be bereft,'
But, furious, the old folk left.
Besides, they had to make some stops
At Smith's and Boots and other shops.

As well as buying pottery
And tickets for the lottery,
They bought a card to send to Fred.
The message ran: *Our love is dead*.

Back home they ate their tea and sighed,
'No one can say we haven't tried.
Oh well, better get the jelly –
Would you please switch on the telly?'

Their excitement began to grow,
Waiting for the lottery show.
The draw was made and soon they shouted,
'We've won, we've won: can't be doubted!'

It took some time to understand
That everything they'd ever planned
Was truly now within their reach.
Gran was almost robbed of speech!

'There's so much good that we can do.
For all our friends and neighbours too!
We must help Tom – yes, and his wife –
They so deserve a better life!'

'Yes,' said Gran, 'but when we're ready.
And just for them – NOT for Freddie.
I wouldn't want that ghastly boy
To even have a single toy.'

Of course, when Freddie heard the news
He quickly came to change his views.
'I love you, Grandpa – love you, Gran.
You know that I'm a Chelsea fan—'

'Let me stop you, Freddie my lad.
You've hurt us both – you drove us mad.
And though we're giving much to many,
You, young man, won't get a penny.'

'But that's **bankles*** and so unfair!
Why's it my fault I like to swear?
You should love me just as I am:
Lovable Freddie – little lamb.'

'Lovable Freddie – little lamb?
What are you like? Why don't
       you scram!
And pardon our words while we scoff,
But, you know what, Freddie,
       just ****† off!'

† In this instance, I decided to use asterisks to mask the word I had in mind. I leave it to your imagination. If in doubt – and especially if you're reading this out aloud in public – then use the word 'beep'.

Cally: Whose Overuse of the word 'Like' led to something she really Didn't Like

A charming girl was Cally Green,
Lovely, friendly, never mean.
In fact she had just one small fault –
Enough, alas, to call a halt
To dreams she had to have the chance
To go to Euro Disney, France.

So what was this 'fault', you might ask,
That saw poor Cally taken to task
By Emily, her only aunt –
The woman with the power to grant
Her greatest wish – however tricky –
To go to France and cuddle Mickey.

Cally liked to use the word 'like'
In her home or out on her bike.
She used this word all of the time,
Which made it a serious crime
For Emily, who liked to preach
When it came to her niece's speech.

'Why **do** you use that awful word?
It is the thousandth time I've heard
You employ the word "like" today.
Do you have nothing else to say?
Do I have to ask Pam Harris
To take **her** daughter to Paris?'

'Sorry, Auntie, like, I, like, **know**
That, like, every time I go
"Like" it's, like, really annoying,
But, like, I'm not, like, enjoying,
Like, using the word like I do.
And you're, like, extra picky too.'

With that, her aunt slammed down
        the phone.
Cally called Friend Jess to moan.
'So I'm, like, sorry. Then she goes,
"Cally, I expect perfect prose,"
Or, like, something like that.
        She's rude
And, like, always in a foul mood.'

'Literally?' said Jess to her friend.
'It'd be literally soooo the end
If *my* aunt literally told me
That I literally wouldn't be
Allowed to go, like, on a treat –
That's literally sort of a cheat.'

Emboldened, Cally called her aunt.
'You think I can help it? I can't.
I've talked to, like, my bestie Jess,
And she's, like, "You don't need
          this stress,"
And I'm, like, "D'er,* think
          I don't know?"
And she goes, like, "Say you won't go."

* A noise made by annoyed or piqued girls.
This is, I'm afraid, the only way I could annotate it.

'But, Auntie, it's, like, so unfair.
I really want to, like, go there.
Can't you ignore what I say?
Like, I just can't talk another way.
It's, like, soooo unfair that you freak
Just because of, like, how I speak.'

'Cally, darling, you must know the truth –
I tell you this despite your youth.
The world will judge you by your voice
And your words – so you have the choice
To talk like me – be a success
Or end up – literally – like Jess.

'This isn't punishment, you know,
But, sorry, darling, you can't go.
I know, I know, it breaks your heart,
But Cally, dear, you have to start
To practise speech around the house.
I'll send a photo of the Mouse.'

Rory: Whose Fussiness when it came to food had Severe Consequences later on in life

For loving mothers there's nothing
 worse
Than having children likely to curse
And wail and scream and act so rude
Just because they've been given *food*!

Yes, my friends, alert all tweeters . . .
We're in the world of faddy eaters!

Rory Cavendish was one such boy:
His mother's cooking gave him no joy.
Whatever she served he wouldn't eat
(Well, not unless it was very sweet).

No cheese, no eggs, no pasta or rice,
No spuds, no salads, or even a slice
Of **anything** healthy – perish the thought!
No wonder that meals were always
      so fraught.

Curry, chilli . . . lasagne with mince
Would cause young Rory to sit there
      and wince.
As for her wonderful Sunday roast –
'Yeugh, I hate that, why can't I have
toast?'

So what other foods did Rory despise?
Er, quite a few, and that's no surprise.
In fact, it might be quicker to cite
The foods he said were 'sort of all right':

Maltesers, gherkins, crisps and jelly
Comprised the contents of Rory's belly.
No vegetables would pass his lips,
Unless you count potato chips.

Somehow he grew up as most children do,
And ended up working as part of the crew
Of a wealthy banker's private yacht
That sailed wherever the weather was hot.

A nice lad was Rory – helpful if quiet,
But he'd never grown out of his
        terrible diet.
Now the only food that Rory could bear
Was cold spaghetti with slices of pear,
And cured salmon – that's gravadlax
(Please don't blame me,
        I just report the facts).

This was fine – the cook found it
        pleasing,
Though Rory suffered a little teasing,
Until, one day, he ran out of luck –
Yes, this was the point disaster struck.

The gorgeous yacht he was proud
        to serve
Hit a reef – there was no time
        to swerve.
The ship was sinking, the alarm
        was sounded,
The banker's toy was truly grounded.

The banker died – let's not mourn
        his loss
(He had, it seems, been a rotten boss);
No, let's focus on the part of the story
That concerns the fate of our
        friend Rory.

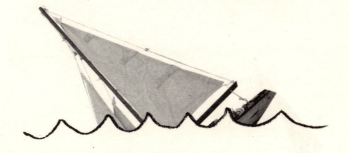

He was washed up on a deserted
      beach,
Miles from home – impossible to reach.
He quickly found water that was fit
      to drink,
But what could he eat?
      He just couldn't think.

Coconuts and yams the trees had
      aplenty,
Fish by the dozen, but his stomach
      stayed empty.
There was even a pig with plenty
      of meat,
But nothing that Rory was able to eat.

So when the eventual rescue boat came,
Rory was dead. We know what's
        to blame!
Pickiness! It drove his mum round
        the bend
And was his undoing right at the end.

So next time you're given food that
        you hate,
Remember poor Rory and his sad,
        hungry fate.

Chelsea: Who eventually learned that Bullying by Exclusion doesn't pay

'You can't come to my party,' Chelsea said.
'If I said yes, it would go to your head.
You'd think that you were as good
    as the rest,
So I really can't have you as a guest.'

'You can't come to my party,' Chelsea said.
'There'll be tea and cake and a massive
    spread.
A conjuror's coming, we'll play lots of games.
I'm inviting Tim and his brother James.'

'You can't come to my party,' Chelsea said.
'Next door's cat is invited
    instead.
There'll be new cartoons
    on a giant screen
And going-home presents
    to turn you green.'

EVERYONE
WELCOME
EXCEPT
YOU!

'You can't come to my party,' Chelsea said.
'You can stay at home and eat jam and bread.
The other children think that you're simple –
And look at your nose – you've got a pimple!'

'You can't come to my party,' Chelsea said.
'Your face is so fat; your hair is too red.
We'll have a swim in the pool if it's warm –
That's me and every child in our form.'

'You can't come to my party,' Chelsea said.
'Even the thought of it fills me with dread.
My friends think you smell and so they
     all say,
If you're invited they simply won't stay.'

'You can't come to my party,' Chelsea said.
'If you did, I would spend the day in bed.
You're useless and boring – that's not
     a lie.
I wish that you would just go home
     and die.'

20 years later

'Can I come to your party?' Chelsea said.
'The Princes are going – so I have read.
I so want to be there, I'm on my knees.
Do say that I can, I'm begging you
please!'

'Hey, come to my party, Chelsea,' I said.
'While you're outside, you can stand on
your head.
I remember taking it on the chin.
Yes, you can come but I won't let you in.'

Jasper Rooney: Who was always Bored and thus grew up to be Intensely Boring

Jasper Rooney was always bored;
His spirits simply never soared.
His parents bought him ev'ry toy
Without receiving any joy.

Jasper wasn't a naughty kid –
He behaved no worse than others
  did –
No toys or games or fun excursion
Offered him the least diversion.

He was so unlike his sister,
Who loved skipping games and Twister,
Plus Monopoly and Cluedo,
Not to mention chess and ludo.

Sometimes his mother barely coped
As Jasper sat around and moped.
'Why can't you find something to do?
You're bored? I'm bored looking at you!'

Jasper's answer remained the same:
'I'm bored and I've played ev'ry game.
There's nothing here for me to do –
The fact I'm bored must mean it's true.'

His mother sighed: 'You're wrong, you
    know.
But if you're bored, then why not go
Play with the others in the park?
You can stay there till it's dark.'

'You just don't get it, do you, Mum?
I hate to sit here on my bum,
But when I'm bored I just don't care
To get up and go anywhere.'

The years passed by and Jasper grew,
But sadly there was nothing new.
To him the world stayed deadly dull:
'I'm really bored out of my skull.'

He managed to do well at school
(The boy was bored – but not a fool).
Soon it was time for Master Rooney
To study Law at Sussex Uni.*

Arriving there for Freshers' Week,
He thought it looked a little bleak.
True, there were clubs and stuff to do,
But nothing changed his jaded view.

He sat around the student halls,
Just staring at the four brick walls.
He was shocked to be ignored,
It's *so* unfair for someone bored!

Too late, in his third year he saw
   The truth that proved a vital flaw.
   A boy who's bored is only storing
   A grown-up who is truly boring.

*A common shortening of the word 'university' which the author loathes but finds useful in the current context.

Chloe: Whose determination to have more Facebook Friends than anyone else Lost her all her Friends

Like many children of her age,
Chloe loves her Facebook page.
But unlike most, poor Chloe seems
To take her Facebook to extremes.

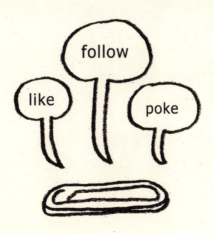

She can't think or cry or chortle
Unless it's through Facebook's portal.
To be online just seems so right
At any time of day or night.

Offline, her world is just a blur:
Her Facebook friends are *real* to her.
They poke her, 'like' her, check her feed,
And hang on every word and deed.

Her total count of friends to date?
Nine hundred and seventy-eight.
Twenty-two more would be just 'grand' –
That's her next status update planned!

Then there's the 'chat' and all the games –
Farmville, The Sims – you know the names.
Facebook's life without the dross.
It's not for you? Then that's your loss!

Chloe thinks she's totally cool,
Blanking all the kids at school
(Except for Emma, a Facebook friend,
Her classmates drive her round the bend).

It's true that bowling sounds like fun,
As does a picnic in the sun.
These she ignores without a flicker:
She craves a world that updates quicker.

So forget that party – nix that meal;
Forgo that concert – no big deal!
Who cares that Chloe has no chums?
She will, you see, when the time comes.

Moral: Friends are people you can count on – not count.

Jason: Whose unpleasantness led to a surprising death

Jason McCaw was a horrible boy;
Trying to teach him was less than a joy
He disrupted all of the lessons in school
He screamed at the teachers –
    broke every rule.

"Jason's bright but just can't focus!"
That was the sort of hocus pocus
The teachers would feed the Mums
    and Dads
All exploring the latest fads
To explain their kids' unpleasantness
Without blame or shame or any distress.

"Our son has got this condition, you see"
They'd tell their friends over a cup of tea.
For if not why would he misbehave?
He had to be suffering from something
        grave.
This was darling Jason, their only child
Who'd never do anything remotely wild

(Well there was the time he scalded
        the cat
But there was nothing intentional in that
It's true he gave his friend a black eye
But that was because he'd told him a lie.
As for the au pair and her litany of woe
"We're sorry, Katja, but you'll have to go.
And yes we can see that you're clearly
        shaken
"But there's no doubt to us that you're
        mistaken")

And that's why Jason was taken to see
An eminent doctor with a PHD
And other initials after his name
That spoke of his skill, his judgment,
        his fame.
Teachers bothered by Jason's behaviour
Hoped this doctor would be their saviour
So long as he got the liquid cosh*
They'd tell the parents any old tosh.

"So tell me, young man, young Jason,
        young J
How precisely can I help you today?"
"I dunno," said Jason and gobbed
        on the floor
His mother and father stared
        at the door.

Soon after the doctor explained what
　　he'd found:
"I'm happy to say that he's basically
　　sound.
He does have his 'problems', as we
　　can all see
But we'll treat that with diet and
　　Vitamin D"

"What's that?" asked his parents
　　"You won't give him drugs?"
The doctor laughed. "No, no – just
　　good food and hugs.
"You could also try a dose of
　　tough love
The iron fist in the velvet glove."

His parents left, suppressing their sighs;
They didn't doubt that the doctor
    was wise
But he hadn't exactly offered a cure
For the pain that their son was forced
    to endure

Then as they made their way to the car,
Their little lad said, "you know it's
    really not far
From here to the nearest computer
    game store –
Where you can buy me Lollipop
    Chainsaw"

"What was that, Jason?" asked father
    with shame
"D'oh, idiot! It's clearly a video game.
I just have to have it before the others.
Tarquin, Sebastian and his brothers"

So off they all went, to make Jason's day
(For they knew if they didn't, they'd
        have to pay
With sulks and tantrums –
        goodness knows what;
And the vilest language from
        their lovely tot).

Once in the shop, with the McCaws resigned
To the nagging for which the layout's
        designed
Jason's eyes were entirely fixed
On a poster for Resident Evil 6
"I absolutely have to have that game,
"Everything else would be far too lame
And you know how difficult I can be
I just need some things to interest me."
Faced with such logic, his parents agreed
This wasn't indulgence, this was just need.

That night he began to tackle the game.
To get to the end – yes, that was his aim.
His parents went to bed at eleven
Well, they both had to be up by seven.
They had no worries at all for their son
In fact, they were thrilled that he
      had begun
To take an interest for more than a minute
In something without wanting to bin it.
They even decided to make no fuss
About the fact that it was eighteen plus

He carried on playing with intensity
He was totally focused as can be.
In fact, his attention was at its peak:
He could hardly breathe; let alone speak.
He was so consumed, playing and
      viewing
It proved to be his fatal undoing.

Jason had never really used his brain
And so now it buckled under the strain.
He wasn't nervous, he wasn't frightened
But he'd never had his senses
    heightened.
Suddenly, Jason could hear feel and see
Better than anyone (yes, you and me)
But something was wrong and giving
    him pain
Whatever was happening to Jason's
    brain!
His neurons were leaking, his
    synapses fried
His cortex had withered and his lobes
    had all died
His head was exploding and he was
    all done.
The McCaws had lost their
    unspeakable son

MORAL:

The brain is an organ that needs
to be tested
And nurtured and fed and
regularly rested.
And being vile is no way to behave
At worst it can lead to an early
grave

*How Ritalin, a drug that is given to subdue children is
known to the teaching profession

Sophie: Whose Australian Inflection caused her to Die in a Fire

A manner of speaking that's become a craze
Puts all of the stress at the end of a phrase.
The Aussie inflection is how it is known
(It just makes me grind my teeth to the bone).

For instance: take Sophie, who talked
  in this *way*?
She'd pitch up her voice on the last words
  she'd *say*?
I'm sure that you're getting the hang
  of this *now*?
A voice that's ascending – annoying,
  and *how*?

What caused all her teachers and parents
    to wonder
Was the fact that she'd not even
    travelled Down Under.
The furthest point south that she'd
    actually been
Was the London suburb of Golders Green.

Why did she talk in that bothersome
        voice?
Nobody knew – it was a matter
        of choice.
Though Sophie should not have to
        take all the blame,
It has to be said that her friends
        were the same.

'You're totes wasting my *minutes*?'
        Amanda would say.
With all of the emphasis going the way
Of the very last word – so silly,
        so strange,
And no one and nothing could get them
        to change.

But making each sentence a question,
    you know,
Has one or two drawbacks as I will
    soon show.
We live in a world that tends to get weary,
Of people who speak as if there's a query.

One evening young Sophie was home
    on her own
Avoiding her homework ('I'm not
    in the *zone*?').
She'd put on the oven to heat up
    her tea
But forgot all about it while watching
    TV.

When all of a sudden she started to choke
And soon realized she was breathing
     in smoke.
'Oh my *God*?' she exclaimed. 'That's,
     like, not a good *sign*?'
So she picked up her phone and she
     dialled 999.

Her call was picked up with
     remarkable speed.
'Emergency services – what do you need?'
Because she was frightened, she
     simply said, *'Fire*?'
(As usual, her voice going higher
     and higher.)

'Yes, fire,' said the man on the end
of the line.
'Do you need assistance?
Is everything fine?'
But Sophie could only reply with
a yelp –
And still it came out like a question:
'*Help*? *Help*?'

The operator was thrown: 'Is there
a doubt?
We're busy and don't really want to
come out
Unless you are sure you can really
see flames
We have to assume that you're just
playing games.'

'I hear what you're saying but
there is a **blaze**?'
Said the poor girl who was by now
in a daze.
'There are **flames**?' she repeated –
a desperate cry
'No, I don't think so,'said the man.
'Now, goodbye.'

The call disconnected – it now was
    too late
To rescue poor Sophie from her
    fiery fate.
But that was too bad – yes, she just
    had to croak.
If only she'd taken more care how
    she spoke.

Postscript: In practice, if there's *any* doubt, the emergency services will always dispatch a fire engine, ambulance or police car. Still, it's worth scaring people if it makes them stop using the Aussie inflection, eh readers?

Sebastian: The Most Annoying Person in the whole world who ended up in a Fitting Occupation

There once was a boy named
    Sebastian Burld –
No one more annoying in all
    of the world:
He'd borrow your biro and suck
    on the top,
He'd tunelessly whistle, refusing
    to stop.

'End of,' he would say, meaning
    'This subject's dead.'
He made fun of boys who were
    gingery-red;
He'd rotate his cap all the way round,
And let his jeans sag right down
    to the ground.

At the movies, he'd turn on his phone
        and he'd text;
He also guessed loudly what was
        happening next
Online he delighted in forwarding spam –
'Any complaints? File under
        "Who gives a damn!"'

The way he spoke annoyed all the
        adults he met;
His surly behaviour made everyone fret.
He would say 'No offence' before giving
        just that,
And tell overweight children to
        'stop being fat'.

He'd demand cash and not sweeties
    on each Halloween;
His language to strangers was
    always obscene.
At football he'd shout when the other
    team scored.
To teachers? Like fingernails scraped
    down the board.

So what happened, you wonder,
    to this ghastly child?
Did he grow up to be more
    obnoxious and wild?
No, he did not, and I'm here to
    tell you the truth:
Sebastian took his chance in
    a polling booth.

That's right, a politician
    is what he became:
A man without principles, feelings
    or shame.
A successful MP – a total obscenity.
I've changed his name
    to protect his identity.

Bethan: Who was Addicted to TV Talent Shows and ended up appearing on one

Whenever he's on, people howl –
I refer, of course, to Simon Cowell.
For myself, I feel a wreck
Whenever I see Ant and Dec.

There's Louis, Dannii, Cheryl C. –
That's not to mention Gary B.
Holden, Walliams – judges both
On programmes that I simply loathe.

Bethan Wells, however, chose
To watch the TV talent shows:
Britain's Got Talent and ***The Voice***,
But ***The X Factor*** was her choice.

Bethan couldn't get enough
Of dancing, singing – all that stuff –
Folk who couldn't bear to toil
To reach the heights of Susan Boyle.

Bethan's best – her favourite part
Was the audition at the start.
She loved to see the judges sneer
While useless acts would shed a tear.

'Rubbish – you've no skill at all!'
'There's the exit – off you crawl!'
'What made you think you could
      get through –
My dog could sing that better than you!'

The judging wasn't fun unless
She could relish their distress:
'Come on, Nicole,' she would shout.
'Throw those lame no-hopers out.'

But even so, she had her dreams,
Unlikely though – or so it seemed:
To sing, to dance – to be on screen –
Perhaps perform before the Queen.

She didn't tell her friends or folks
For fear that they would all make jokes.
So she thought it would be better
If she sent in a secret letter.

It worked! A phone call:
          'Please come down
To an audition in your town.'
She told her bestie Kim the news,
And then went off to buy some shoes.

No TV judges were in sight;
As she stepped out into the light.
'OK, Beth, let's hear your song.
Just a bit – don't take too long!'

She sang *Umbrella* by Rihanna,
Unaccompanied by piano.
You didn't need to know the clef
To gather that she was tone deaf.

So you might find it odd to hear
Researchers say, 'Great, Beth – we're
Sending you to the next round.
Simon's going to love your sound!'

Bethan walked out upon a cloud:
Leona Lewis, Girls Aloud . . .
She was going all the way –
Who knew where her destiny lay?

She told her friends, her mum and dad,
'I'm going to win – aren't you glad?
The man said Simon had decreed
A voice like mine is what they need.'

The days dragged so slowly past
Until her big day came at last.
She waited in an endless queue
With everyone who'd been put through:

Comics practising their sets;
Kiddies, grans and dancing pets;
Singers belting out their track
And every kind of novelty act.

She'd see rejected people cry.
'I loved it, it was great!' they'd lie.
She vowed that wouldn't be her fate
Once she got through this awful wait.

At last she heard her own name called:
'Bethan!' Simon Cowell drawled.
This was the entertainment tsar
Who would at last make her a star.

'Hi, I'm Bethan and tonight
I'd like to sing J. Lo's *Get Right*.'
'OK,' said Simon, 'do please start.
We're here to suffer for your art.'

The backing track pumped out its beat;
Bethan tripped over her feet.
She started singing: it was *worse* –
The judges couldn't help but curse.

'You're dreadful – yes, you really are.
That's why we stopped you on that bar.
The worst performance seen on earth –
I thought a cat was giving birth!'

The second judge was just as tough:
'I'll keep it short – enough, enough!
As bad as anything in years.
I wish I'd thought to plug my ears!'

'That was simply music hell –
Only as torture could *that* sell.
You killed that song with a cleaver!
You make a crow sound like a diva!'

Crying, Bethan fled the stage,
But after tears there came the rage.
'They told me that they loved my voice,
So why pick me – they had a choice.'

Aha, she thought, *the penny drops:*
They want the ones who will be flops.
It's not by chance that people fail –
It's what they want: to hear us wail!

I'm going to change – be less flash,
And not watch any telly trash.
And now I know how cruel it is,
I promise to stay out the biz.*

Bethan proves it's not too late
For people to escape their fate.
And please don't laugh at those who go
On to the TV talent show.

* As show business is known to insiders.

Tarquin Yardley: Whose Disobedience proved to be his Undoing

Tarquin Yardley, nine years old,
Would never do as he was told,
For Tarquin was a spoiled brat,
Refusing to do this or that –

And not because of wrong or right,
But just because he loved to fight
With adults, teachers and his mum,
Who never smacked him on his bum.

Despite his daily provocations.
There was this one time at the station
When she yelled, 'Tarc, no, not
          the track!'
Contrary Tarquin stepped right back

And teetered there, about to fall
Onto the rails . . . the closest call!
But even then, Mum stayed her hand
(As smacking kids is rightly banned).

Tarquin was the same at school,
Disobeying every rule.
'Don't run indoors', 'Don't talk in class',
And there was Tarquin, bold as brass,

Doing absolutely the reverse
Of every order with a curse.
The act of being less than willing
Was something Tarquin found
     so thrilling

Disrespecting teachers? Fun!
He knew that nothing could be done
To stop his anti-social ways
(It's somewhat tricky nowadays).

His mum and dad were at wits' end:
'We've got to help our Tarquin mend
His ways before he comes unstuck –
Or hurts himself or runs amok!'

'Perhaps we should ask Dr Dougall,
Or better still, look on Google?'

So here, my friends, is what they did
In a desperate final bid
To cure their troubled younger boy.
They considered every ploy:

Electric shocks and pills and diets –
Anything for peace and quiet.
And when they just could take no more
They found a site that Tarq's dad swore
Would put an end to all their woes:

'It's brilliant, Sue – here's how it goes!

Let's say he has to go to bed:
You tell him that you have a dread
Of him just going off to sleep.
It won't be possible to keep
The boy from dashing to his room –
No more rowing, no more gloom!
All we need do to lift this curse
Is simply nag him in reverse!'

Well – at first it worked a treat:
'Tarquin, go play in the street!'
Would absolutely guarantee
That he just stay on the settee.

Likewise, 'Tarquin, please don't shower!'
Would see him rush to scrub and scour
His body till it was pristine –
Without the need to make a scene.
His mum learned how to pull his strings
By turning round the sense of things.

One day as she was going out
She tried a classic turnabout:
'Tarquin, while I'm gone I'm keen
That you by no means try to clean;
Your bedroom's in a lovely state –
It's filthy, grimy – really great!
Leave those dirty plates and cups,
And please don't touch the washing up!'

She smiled to herself as she went –
This new approach was heaven sent!

Alas! This story has a hook –
Like many children in this book,
Tarquin was too bad *not* to die
(Gather close – I'll tell you why).
For these are cautionary tales,
And that's why they must end in wails.

Well, I'll show her! young Tarquin
        thought;
He went out to the shed and brought
The hosepipe in, and hooked it to
The cold tap in the upstairs loo.

She wants my bedroom grubby, eh?
I'll blast that nasty dirt away!
I bet she never thought I'd thwart her
With super pressure jets of water!

And with a grin he turned his hose
On stinking piles of underclothes.
He sprayed the walls, he drenched
     the floor,
He soaked the ceiling and the door
Until the water level rose
To lap at Tarquin's naked toes.
But this is what he'd not foreseen:
His electronic toys, machines
And gadgets all began to swim –
And what was more – they were all
     plugged in!

A flash, some smoke – and all
     that juice
Short-circuited and cooked his goose.
I shan't describe his horrid pains
As all the voltage from the mains
Zapped through him like a
     lightning bolt;

The disobedient little dolt.
Happy to die at a youthful age
If only it caused his parents rage.
And so it was that he perished
True to values that he cherished
Cunning, spoilt to his final breath,
His was a truly fitting death.

Clara: Whose crush on an Athlete led to Sporting Disappointment

Let me tell you about Clara,
Who had a crush on Mo Farah,
The British runner who found fame
In the 2012 Olympic Games.

Clara loved this running man:
To be like him – that was her plan –
And thus become a record beater
In the fifteen hundred metres.

Off she went to her local club
(And here, alas, must come the rub),
For while she wanted just to run,
The man in charge said, 'Can't be done.

'I don't want to give you a fright,
But you aren't . . . well . . . exactly
    light.
And since the Games we're overbooked,
So that is why you're overlooked.'

Clara, though undoubtedly spunky,
Was, indeed, a little chunky.
Though hardly in an obese state,
She really was quite overweight.

Now here the author must confess
That he himself is somewhat less
Skinny or slender than his peers
(He hasn't seen his toes in years!).

With massive tum and chafing thighs,
Yup, Mitchell's eaten ALL the pies,
And though his face could not be finer,
There are fewer chins in China.

But just as Clara reached the door,
The man in charge said, 'Please wait
    – you're
Welcome to try another sport:
There are many here being taught.

'You could try some weights – put the
    shot,
Or ride a bike like Laura Trott.
You might try boxing – or table-
    tennis,
Or throw a javelin like Jess Ennis.'

Clara listened then shook her head.
'I want to run like Mo,' she said.
'And even if I'd be no good,
At least I'd be the best I could.'

So she left – went back to her house.
She phoned her friends and had a
    grouse
About the fact she couldn't run –
'Which means my Farah dream is
    done.

'No more athletics, no more Mo.
I want to *run* – not punch or throw.
Don't want to *jump* or ride a bike –
I want to do the sport I like.'

So that was that. What might have
    been?
If Clara weren't a drama queen,
Would she have had success? Plenty!
Shot-put gold in 2020 . . .

Bill: Whose ability to Fart ended in Tears

This is the tale of a boy named Bill
Who found that he could fart at will.
He could pop one out any time of day –
At home, at school, or even at play.

Silent but deadly or loud as a gun,
Bill was an expert whose bottom
   could stun
A skunk with its terrible gaseous pong –
The odour was just incredibly strong.

The wind that his awesome buttocks
   could pass
Had made him the central attraction
   in class.
His school friends would beg him
   'Fire one off!'
As simply as someone doing a cough.

In Geography, Science, English and
    French,
Teachers puzzled the source of the
    stench.
They never suspected the flatulent skill
Of that expert erupter, fartacious Bill.

Bill's problems began when, to amuse
    the boys,
He started to crank up the level of noise.
Now when he farted it was truly grim,
And no doubt at all that it came
    straight from him.

Still his poor teacher was wary to act
When harassing a child could see her
    get sacked.
Instead, for self-preservation she chose
To open the window and bury her nose.

But then came the day when he
        pushed it too far –
I mean that for real, I'm afraid,
        ha ha!
He'd prepared letting go a fart or two,
Which would have been fine –
but *he followed through!*

There was nothing at all the
poor boy could do
As he sat there awash in an ocean of poo.
It ran down his legs and pooled on the floor,
While all of his classmates ran
straight to the door.

Bill and his teacher were left
        on their own.
'Well, Bill, that was silly,
        as you have just shown.
Go to the nurse, get a note
        for your mum,
And promise we'll hear no more
        from your bum.'

Callum: Who was a Dreadful Bully until he received his Come-uppance

Callum Jones liked bullying boys.
Like it? He loved it – more than toys!
He pulled their hair and twisted
    their ears,
And laughed as they were left in tears.

He pinched and punched, poked and
    bashed,
He clinched and crunched, choked
    and smashed.
Every poor lad who came his way
Always had cause to rue that day.

His victims – mostly younger lads –
Would run off home to mums and dads
Who, in turn, would phone the school
To ask about the bullying rule.

The school would always say the same:
'Zero tolerance is our aim.
Bullying is a wicked crime
Which will be punished all the time.

BUT . . .

'We are child-centred and therefore designed
To leave no single child behind.
So though we frown on Callum's acts,
We're bound – for his sake – to be lax.'

Parents were shocked but soon found out
That in such matters they had no clout.
The school had said their hands were tied,
So that was it – all cut and dried.

This left young Callum free to do
Everything he wanted to
(Not including things most chilling
Like torturing and actual killing).

Nevertheless, he made life vile
For Harry, Charlie, Jack and Kyle –
To name but four unlucky chaps
Whose lives were marred by daily scraps.

And then one day a new boy came.
His name was Alfie: he looked quite tame.
So Callum tried his usual tricks,
Like Chinese burns and ankle kicks.

At first young Alfie looked dismayed –
He thought playgrounds were where
     you **played**.

He wasn't looking for any woe;
He merely wanted this pest to go.
Callum thought, ***This kid is weak!***
I know just how to make him shriek
With something gross – really edgy.
Aha, he thought, ***I'll try a wedgie!***

Alfie, however, had other plans:
He parried Callum and grabbed his hands.
'Hey, you, back off, leave me alone!'
Callum was shocked and nearly thrown.

But then he stopped and gathered his wits:
He wasn't going to call it quits.
He ran at him with flailing fists,
But Alfie simply caught his wrists.

Stupid Callum came bouncing back
And tried to land a blow or smack.
Alfie punched him right on the jaw,
But still the bully wanted more.

Callum yelped and spat in his eye,
Screaming out loud, 'You're gonna die!'
This pushed Alfie over the edge,
So he shoved Callum into a hedge.

The other children laughed and cheered
To see the boy that they had feared
Finally beaten in a fair fight:
A bully bested – what a sight!

Callum went home – his parents shrieked.
'There's this boy Alfie,' Callum sneaked.
So Callum's parents phoned the school
To ask about the bullying rule.

Of course the school said just the same:
'Zero tolerance is our aim.
Bullying is a wicked crime
Which will be punished every time.

BUT . . .

'We are child-centred and so designed
To leave no single child behind.
So though we frown on Alfie's acts,
We're bound – for his sake – to be lax.'

Callum cried and made a fuss,
But bullies' tears don't worry us.
Thanks to Alfie, play is splendid
And Callum's evil reign has ended.

Jeremy Smythe:
Whose Snobbery proved
to be a Liability

Jeremy Smythe was a terrible snob
Who considered himself ahead of the mob.
He lived with his parents in
    Eaton Square –
Anywhere else was too common to bear.

Jeremy Smythe was a terrible snob:
No one he knew had ever needed
    a job.
At ten years old, he was set up
    for life –
Eton, Oxford, then a suitable wife.

Jeremy Smythe was a terrible snob;
He disdained the boys named Darren
    and Rob.
In fact, no boy was sufficiently fine,
Though he knew a Tristram at
    number nine.

Jeremy Smythe was a terrible snob,
Whose maid had to take the corn
    off the cob.
Pronounce his name wrong and
    he'd get in a strop –
He could not be prevented
    from blowing his top.

Jeremy Smythe was
    a terrible snob:
'A wristwatch?
    How common, I wear a gold fob.
And as for my cousins, they're lower
    than me –
My mum married "up" with my father,
    you see.'

Jeremy Smythe was a terrible snob:
The folk in the street caused his
     temples to throb.
Their language made his prejudice
     harden –
They always said 'what' instead of
     'beg pardon'.

Jeremy Smythe was a terrible snob,
But an unforeseen tragedy moved him
     to sob.
The family lost all their money
     in shares,
So they're all wiped out – including
     the heirs.

Jeremy Smythe is a terrible snob,
A bone idle, useless, impoverished slob.
He's entirely too grand to make use
of his brains,
So his snobbery is, sadly, all that remains.

Natasha Wilkinson: Who couldn't stop Boasting and so missed out on a Round-the-World Cruise

Natasha Wilkinson just loved to preen:
'My mummy is a close friend of the Queen,
We live in a mansion and have a yacht –
I can't think of anything we haven't got.'

The truth was that she was an ordinary
    girl
Who *wasn't* related to a baron or earl.
Nor did her family own half the coast,
As this foolish child was given to boast.

Yes, boasting, Natasha's conspicuous trait,
A worrying thing in a girl of just eight.
She swanked and she peacocked and gave
    herself airs,
Pretending her family were all millionaires.

Sometimes her stories were utterly crazy:
'I fired my servant for being so lazy.'
Her classmates at school fell under her spell.
She was so convincing – you just couldn't
    tell!

They'd go home and report on all that
    she'd said:
'Natasha's got golden sheets on her bed!'
Their parents decided not to find fault:
'I think I'd take that with a pinch of salt.'

So that's how Natasha spent all of
    her days
Embellishing life in improbable ways.
She couldn't have known she was
    going to lose
The chance to go on a round-the-world
    cruise.

It happened like this: a girl that she
    knew
Had parents who *did* earn a million
    or two.
And when they decided to go on a trip
They chartered the world's most
    luxurious ship.

'Tell you what, Jane,' they said to their
    daughter,
'You're welcome to bring a friend on the
    water.'
'I'll take Natasha – if that is OK.
She's lots of fun and we do love to play.'

'I don't think so, my dear,' came her
    mother's reply.
'Didn't you say she was off to Shanghai?'
'You're right, Mum, she's rich' – and
    with that Jane smiled –
'So yes, I'll invite a needier child.'

Jane – with her friend – disappeared
    for a year.
Natasha's boasting had cost her so dear,
And as she shivered in the winter frost,
At last she knew what her silliness cost.

Simon: Who never lifted the Toilet Seat and so suffered Disappointment

A nasty shock that's hard to beat
Is sitting on a wet loo seat.

The family of Simon Kray
Experienced this every day,

For all the time this pesky clown
Would do his wee with the
      seat down.

His mother said, 'This isn't fair!
Your wee-wee's going everywhere.'

Simon smiled, the little pup,
But didn't leave the loo seat up.

His father tried a little chat;
His sisters plotted worse than that.

But even so – with tears from Mum –
They all still suffered a soggy bum.

His father hatched a cunning plan
To guarantee a drier can:

He bought his son a brand-new bike
With sixteen gears – what's not to like!

Of course, there was just one condition:
Loo seat in the 'up' position.

'You only can enjoy this treat
If you respect the toilet seat.

'And not just now – for ever, or
The bike goes right back to the store.'

Well, for a week or so it worked:
Dry bums all round with no one irked.

You know old habits – they die hard,
And one day Si was off his guard.

He used the loo – went off to play,
And left the seat with lots of spray.

His mother cursed her wretched son:
His father's plan had come undone.

Should they give him one more chance,
Or should they take the tougher stance?

Mother, being kind and tender,
Said, 'Poor boy, it's just his gender.'

His sisters said, 'A deal's a deal –
He has to know how others feel.'

It was for Dad to make the call;
The bike was standing in the hall.

'Look, Si, I know this isn't nice,
But, yes, you have to pay the price.

'We asked you nicely just to do
Your best to leave a drier loo.

'The bicycle was only bought
As a desperate last resort.

'The bike goes back. That's not the end.
No more treats if you re-offend.

'This should be your daily goal:
Always hit the toilet bowl.'

Gilly Adams:
Who Bit her Nails
and so lost out

Gilly Adams bites her nails
All the time – she never fails
To bite them to the very quick
Which makes her friends feel
rather sick.

Even when her nails are black
She still sees them as a snack.
Chewing nails isn't silly
For total addicts like young Gilly.

Her mother says, 'Don't you know,
By not letting your nails grow
You'll make yourself look less than smart?
I hope you take these words to heart.'

Gilly shakes her head and chews.
'I'm not the sort of baby whose
Mum can tell her what to do.
I'm ten years old now – not two!'

Her father tries, 'Now listen here:
This habit's horrid, and so we're
To paint your nails with special stuff
That makes them taste so very rough.'

'Am I bothered? Am I hell!
I'll get used to any smell.
You see, it's my human right
To pick and choose just what I bite.

'I don't stop you playing squash.
I don't stop Mum talking posh.
I haven't bothered anyone,
So who are you to stop my fun?'

'OK, Gilly,' her father sighs.
'You know best – you are so wise.
Keep on biting, I don't care.
Chew on mine, they're going spare!'

In later life, when she's at work,
Biting her nails with a smirk,
Her new boss calls her in to say:
'You're promoted – come this way.'

Gilly's thrilled and tells him so.
'It's well-deserved, now you must go
To New York and Los Angeles.
Fly first class – you're the bees' knees!

'I don't want to make you squirm,
But you'll represent the firm.
Looking good will help with sales –
But, wait – yeuggh – what ghastly nails!

'I expected you to be well-groomed,
But with nails like that we're
        surely doomed.
I'm sorry, but the offer's gone.
You stay here – I'm sending John.'

So Gilly Adams was left to rue
Her dream-destroying need to chew.
She wouldn't now be so sad
If she'd listened to her dad,
And not been quite so highly strung
But quit her habit while still young

**Moral: If the young only knew;
if the old only could.**

William Tobias Patterson-Meads, who was a Really Nice Guy and so became an Immense Success

AN EPILOGUE

You probably think that every verse
Of mine will be grotesque or worse;
Tales of kids who wouldn't learn
And so were set to drown or burn.
Tiresome brats without redemption –
All of them doomed with no exemption.
The only thing left for me to append
Is quite how they meet their
      well-deserved end.

So it gives me pleasure to relate the deeds
Of William Tobias Patterson-Meads,
Who couldn't have been nicer than he was
– A marvellous boy – if only because
He had the best manners of any child
And was never once surly or sulky or wild.

Of course the adults who met him
     were charmed,
And yet his contemporaries were also
     disarmed.
For William was just the best of guys:
You could tell that from the warmth
     in his eyes.

So what became of this marvellous chap?
How did he suffer? What was his mishap?
When it comes to him we have to invert
(Plus, my title had a spoiler alert).
No, William Tobias Patterson-Meads,
By dint of his niceness . . .
     simply succeeds.
Enjoying a life that is full to the brim
Of wonderful things and not the least grim.
So is there a moral to *this* tale?
     Why, yes!
Be a good child, act well; do your best!

CODA

And finally – and with apologies to Paul Simon* – a poem for all those of you who might wish to avoid finding themselves in any future volume of such poems

Just be jolly, Holly
Don't be silly, Lily
Please be tidy, Heidi
Show no malice, Alice
Just be canny, Annie

Don't say "fair play", Shay
Nor "I was like", Mike
Don't say "you know", Joe
Don't say "chillax", Max
Stop saying "soz", Loz

Don't be waily, Kayleigh
Don't nag for money, Honey
Don't be lairy, Mary
Don't be snarly, Charlie
Don't be screwy, Louis

Put down that phone, Joan
Don't send on spam, Sam
Don't be a troll, Sol
Try to behave, Dave
Learn how to give, Liv

Don't make a mess, Jess
Be a good pal, Hal
Never be mean, Dean
Tidy up your scrawl, Paul
Try not to be slack, Zac

Just go out and play, Faye
Read a good book, Brooke
And never be rude, Jude
No need to pose, Rose
Don't be too shrill, Gill

Watch the rage, Paige
No need to sigh, Skye
Don't always be late, Kate
Don't pull that face, Grace
Don't be too shrill, Will
Don't play rough games, James
Don't be too grim, Jim
Don't forget to wash, Josh
Go with the flow, Mo

*A brilliant American singer/songwriter whose song
50 Ways To Leave Your Lover inspired this poem